A WHOLE BOOK OF REASONS YOU'RE MY BFF

1

You are the best

____

in the entire world.

2

I can always count on you to

____________________________________.

3

And to make sure I don't

______________________________________.

4

You always tell me
the truth about

______________________________.

5

Your advice is always so

_________________________________.

6

I wish I had one-tenth of your

______________________________.

7

You have impeccable taste in

________________________________.

8

It makes up for
your terrible taste in

______________________________________.

9

You always know exactly
what to do when I'm

______________________________.

10

I'd be totally lost without your

____________________________________.

11

Your

____

will always make me laugh.

12

I enjoy bragging to
other people about your

______________________________.

13

In the Yearbook Superlatives
of Life, you win Best

_______________________________________.

14

will always remind me of you.

15

Who else would be willing to

____

with me?

16

You make everything
so much more

____.

17

If I had a million dollars,
I'd buy you a

____.

18

You always make me feel so

_______________________________.

19

You're more

____

than anyone I know.

20

You should really be
a professional

______________________________.

21

I love how much
you care about

______________________________________.

22

I love how you literally
couldn't care less about

________________________________.

23

I will forever be
grateful for your

____.

24

The way you

____

is truly an art form.

25

When we're old, I hope we still

______________________________.

26

I'll never forget the time we

______________________________________.

27

If you ever get arrested,
it will probably be for

______________________________________.

28

You know all my

____

and you still like me.

29

We could never explain

____

to anyone else.

30

Without you, I would probably

_______________________________________.

I Love

YOU!

FILL IN THE Love®

Created, published, and distributed by Em & Friends™
11111 Jefferson Blvd. #5167
Culver City, CA 90231
emandfriends.com
Em & Friends is a trademark of Knock Knock LLC
Fill in the Love is a registered trademark of Knock Knock LLC

Printed in China

FSC www.fsc.org
MIX
Paper from responsible sources
FSC™ C008047

ISBN: 9781642446661
UPC: 812729027165

10 9 8 7